"You're late, Bert!"
"Sorry, Sir."
"Where were you, Bert?"

"Er...I was helping a little girl to find her mummy."

"You're late again, Bert!"
"Sorry, Sir."
"Where were you, Bert?"

"Er...I was helping a lady to find her purse."

"You're late again, Bert!"
"Sorry, Sir."
"Where were you, Bert?"

"Er...I was helping a furry caterpillar to find a leaf."

"You're late again, Bert!"
"Sorry, Sir."
"Where were you, Bert?"

"Er...I was helping a thirsty dog to find a drink."

"You're late again, Bert!"
"Sorry, Sir."
"Where were you, Bert?"

"Er…I was helping a little boy to find a birthday party."

"You're late again, Bert!"
"Sorry, Sir."
"Where were you, Bert?"

"Er...I was helping a bird to find its nest."

"You're late again, Bert!"
"Sorry, Sir."
"Where were you, Bert?"

"Er...I was helping a worm to find some earth."

"You're late again, Bert!"
"Sorry, Sir."
"Where were you, Bert?"

"Er...I was helping a nurse to find her hospital."

"You're late again, Bert!"
"Sorry, Sir."
"Where were you, Bert?"

"Er...I was helping a turtle to find a pond."

"You're late again, Bert!"
"Sorry, Sir."
"Where were you, Bert?"

"Er...I was helping a mermaid to find a pearl."

"You're late again, Bert!"
"Sorry, Sir."
"Where were you, Bert?"

"Er... I was helping a clown to find the circus."

"Don't be late again, Bert!"
"No, Sir."
"If you're late again, Bert, I will help you find a lot of extra work."

"You're early, Bert!"